Edition Schott

Silvius Leopold Weiss
1686 – 1750

Anthology of Selected Pieces

for Guitar
für Gitarre

Transcribed and edited by /
Transkribiert und bearbeitet von
Raymond Burley

ED 12320
ISMN M-2201-1522-6

www.schott-music.com

Mainz · London · Madrid · New York · Paris · Prag · Tokyo · Toronto
© 1993 SCHOTT MUSIC Ltd., London · Printed in Germany

Contents/Inhalt

Preface   iii

Vorwort   iv

Notes on the Revision   v

Anmerkungen zur Bearbeitung   v

1. Ouverture   1

2. Fantasie   8

3. Tombeau sur la Mort de Mur. Comte d'Logy   13

4. Capricio   17

5. Ciacona   22

6. Fuga   28

7. Tombeau sur la Mort de M: Cajetan Baron d'Hartig   33

8. Passagaille   36

The greater part of the surviving lute music of Silvius Leopold Weiss (1686–1750) is to be found in two autograph manuscript collections now located in the British Library, London, and the Sächsisches Landesbibliothek, Dresden. The works contained in this present anthology are taken exclusively from the London source (*Lbl*, Add. MS 30387). Many of the pieces were originally grouped by common key, and it is to be assumed that the composer intended them to be performed as suites; however, it is from the number of unrelated pieces in this source that most of the works in this anthology are taken—the exceptions being *Ciacona*, which belongs to the tenth 'suite' and *Passagaille* from the fourteenth. In my opinion the set of eight pieces offered here represents Weiss at his most inspired.

Weiss composed for a lute with thirteen courses (pairs of strings). The extended lower range of the instrument, together with its radically different tuning, necessitates alterations in transcription for the guitar such as raising some bass notes by an octave and, occasionally, transposing the piece to a more accommodating key.

The symbols for certain types of embellishment were placed above, below or alongside the affected note in the original MSS; the precise meaning of these is unclear as Weiss gives no explanation regarding their interpretation.

Ruggero Chiesa in *S. L. Weiss. Intavolatura di Liuto* (Edizioni Suvini Zerboni, Milan, 1967), replaces two of Weiss's original symbols, ⊃ and ⊂, with the visually clearer ∩ and ∪; this latter notation is used in the present anthology.

My suggestions for the realization of Weiss's ornamentation symbols are:

∩ = an ornament—e.g., an appoggiatura or trill—approached from above

∪ = an ornament approached from below

♩♪ = the two notes are struck simultaneously and the smaller note is released, or damped, immediately

⁓ = vibrato

X = a wider, more exaggerated, vibrato or a mordent

The unexplained sign ⌐ placed within the chords at the opening of *Tombeau sur la Mort de Mur. Comte d'Logy* probably indicates arpeggiation.

All Weiss's symbols have been included in the score; those that cannot be realized on the guitar—using the given fingering—are shown in square brackets.

The figure *8* placed below certain bass notes shows that the note was originally an octave lower in the MS. Where the *8* sign is shown beneath a chord of two or more parts it refers only to the *lowest* note of the chord.

Editorial slurs are set as dotted lines thus ⌁ and are placed next to the noteheads; Weiss's left-hand slur markings (legatos) have been retained in this edition in normal music type and are placed close to the stems/beams.

Editorial alterations to chord spacing and position, etc., are detailed in the Notes on the Revision below.

Standard guitar nomenclature is used throughout this anthology with the addition of two less common directions: the pivot *barré* and the diagonal *barré*. The pivot *barré* (indicated as 'pivot') is suggested for two purposes: to facilitate the movement to—or from—a conventional *barré*, or to assist the left-hand first finger to move smoothly from a position on the treble strings to a new position on a lower string. The diagonal *barré*—notated, e.g., II/I—suggests that the left-hand first finger covers two frets simultaneously, leaving other fingers free for use elsewhere.

It will be apparent that the suggested guitar fingering will not always allow the notes to be sustained for their printed duration. The full values are shown to indicate the musical intention; players wishing to alter fingerings to adhere strictly to the given note values are, of course, at liberty to do so.

Raymond Burley

Notes on the Revision

The original chord spacings/placements in Weiss's lute tablature which—for obvious technical reasons—I have not attempted in the transcriptions for guitar, are shown on pages v and vi. The examples relating to Nos. 1, 2, 3, 5 and 7 have been transposed to the keys of the transcriptions.

Der größte Teil der überlieferten Lautenmusik von Silvius Leopold Weiss (1686–1750) ist in zwei autographen Manuskriptsammlungen enthalten, die sich jetzt in der British Library, London, und der Sächsischen Landesbibliothek, Dresden, befinden. Die Werke der vorliegenden Anthologie stammen ausschließlich aus der Londoner Quelle (*Lbl*, Add. MS 30387). Viele Stücke der gleichen Tonart waren ursprünglich in Gruppen zusammengefaßt. Es läßt sich daher vermuten, daß der Komponist die Absicht hatte, sie als Suiten aufzuführen. Die Mehrzahl der Stücke dieser Anthologie stand jedoch im Original in keinem Zusammenhang – mit Ausnahme der *Ciacona*, die zur zehnten „Suite" gehört, und der *Passagaille* aus der vierzehnten Suite. Die acht in dieser Sammlung veröffentlichten Stücke beweisen meiner Meinung nach die besondere Kreativität von Weiss.

Weiss komponierte für eine Laute mit dreizehn Saitenpaaren. Der erweiterte, tiefere Umfang des Instruments sowie seine grundlegend verschiedene Stimmung erfordern Änderungen in der Übertragung für Gitarre. So müssen zum Beispiel einige Baßnoten um eine Oktave nach oben versetzt werden; auch mußten manche Stücke gelegentlich in eine bequemere Tonart übertragen werden.

Die Zeichen für bestimmte Verzierungen stehen in den Autographen über, unter oder neben der betroffenen Note; ihre genaue Bedeutung ist jedoch unklar, da Weiss keine Hinweise zu ihrer Interpretation gibt.

Ruggero Chiesa ersetzt in *S. L. Weiss. Intavolatura di Liuto* (Edizioni Suvini Zerboni, Mailand 1967) zwei von Weiss' Symbolen (⊃ und ⊂) durch die anschaulicheren ∩ und ∪; die letztere Schreibweise wurde auch in der vorliegenden Anthologie verwendet.

Ich schlage vor, Weiss' Verzierungen wie folgt auszuführen:

∩ = eine Verzierung von oben, z. B. ein Vorschlag oder ein Triller

∪ = eine Verzierung von unten

♩♪ = beide Noten werden zugleich angeschlagen, wobei die kleinere Note sofort losgelassen oder gedämpft wird

〰 = vibrato

X = ein längeres, stärkeres Vibrato oder ein Pralltriller

Das Symbol ⌒, das in den ersten Akkorden am Anfang von *Tombeau sur la Mort de Mur. Comte d'Logy* vorkommt, bedeutet wahrscheinlich eine Akkordbrechung.

Alle von Weiss verwendeten Zeichen erscheinen im Notentext. Diejenigen, die auf der Gitarre mit dem vorgegebenen Fingersatz nicht realisierbar sind, erscheinen in eckigen Klammern.

Eine *8* unter bestimmten Baßnoten bedeutet, daß die Note im Manuskript ursprünglich eine Oktave tiefer gespielt wurde. Steht die *8* neben einem zwei- oder mehrstimmigen Akkord, so bezieht sie sich nur auf die *tiefste* Note im Akkord.

Vom Herausgeber ergänzte Bögen erscheinen als punktierte Linien neben den Notenköpfen. Weiss' Legato-Bögen für die linke Hand wurden in dieser Ausgabe in normalem Druck beibehalten und erscheinen neben den Hälsen bzw. Balken.

Änderungen des Herausgebers bezüglich der Anordnung und der Lage von Akkorden usw. werden unten im Revisionsbericht eingehend beschrieben.

In dieser Anthologie wurde die übliche Gitarrennomenklatur benutzt unter Hinzufügung von zwei weniger geläufigen Anweisungen: dem gedrehten (pivot) *Barré-Griff* und dem diagonalen *Barré-Griff*. Der gedrehte *Barré-Griff* (gekennzeichnet als „pivot") dient zwei Zwecken: um die Bewegung von einem gewöhnlichen *Barré-Griff* weg oder auf einen gewöhnlichen *Barré-Griff* hin zu erleichtern, oder um dem ersten Finger der linken Hand zu helfen, lückenlos von einer Position auf der Melodiesaite zu einer neuen auf einer tieferen Saite überzugehen. Der diagonale *Barré-Griff* – z. B. als II/I notiert – legt nahe, daß der erste Finger der linken Hand zwei Bünde zugleich ergreift und damit die anderen Finger für andere Griffe freiläßt.

Natürlich läßt der vorgeschlagene Fingersatz es nicht immer zu, daß die Noten für die angegebene Dauer ausgehalten werden können. Die tatsächliche Länge wurde angegeben, um die musikalische Absicht zu verdeutlichen. Spieler, die die Fingersätze ändern möchten, um die vorgegebenen Notenwerte zu befolgen, können dies selbstverständlich tun.

Raymond Burley

Anmerkungen zur Bearbeitung

Auf Seiten v und vi werden die originalen Akkordabstände bzw. -stellungen der Lautentabulatur von Weiss gezeigt, die ich aus naheliegenden technischen Gründen nicht für die Transkription für Gitarre verwendet habe. Die Beispiele, die sich auf Nr. 1, 2, 3, 5 und 7 beziehen, wurden in die jeweilige Tonart der Übertragungen versetzt.

Notes on the Revision/Anmerkungen zur Bearbeitung

1. Ouverture

bar 5

b. 8

b. 10

b. 11

b. 13

b. 61

b. 108

2. Fantasie

b. 6, measured section

3. Tombeau

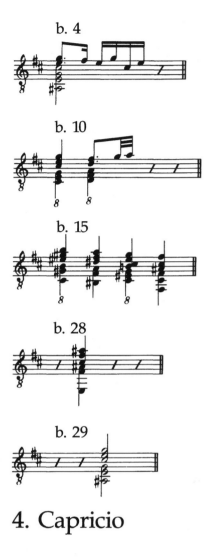

b. 4

b. 10

b. 15

b. 28

b. 29

4. Capricio

b. 8

b. 27

b. 28

b. 49

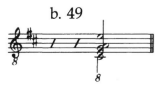

5. Ciacona

6. Fuga

7. Tombeau

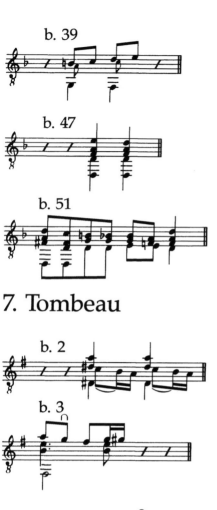

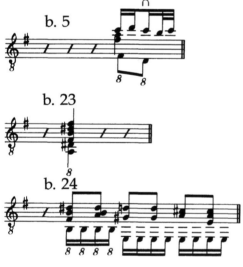

8. Passagaille

Anthology of Selected Pieces
Ausgewählte Werke

Silvius Leopold Weiss
(1686–1750)

Transcribed and edited for Guitar by/
Für Gitarre transkribiert und herausgegeben von
Raymond Burley

1. Ouverture

Original key: B flat Major

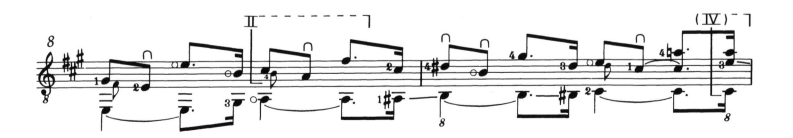

© 1993 Schott Music Ltd., London

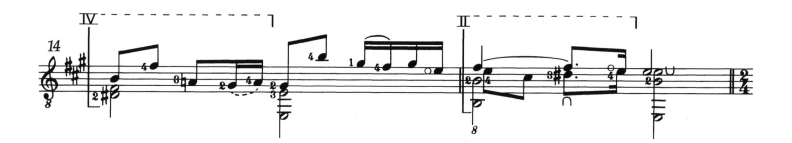

Allegro

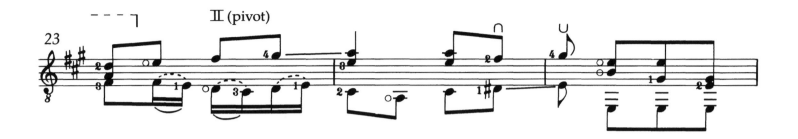

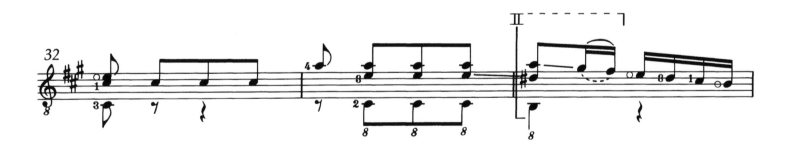

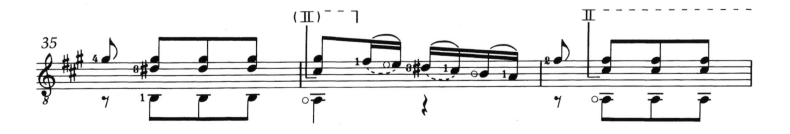

4

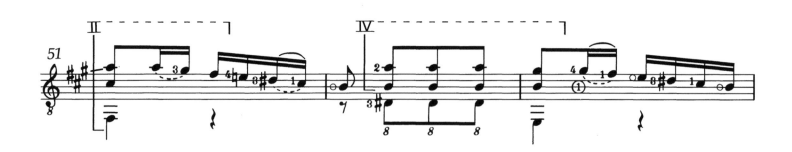

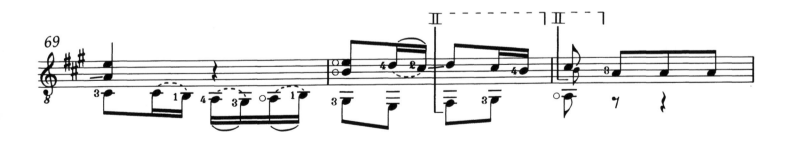

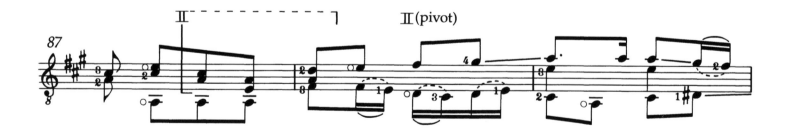

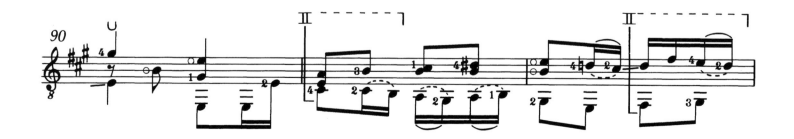

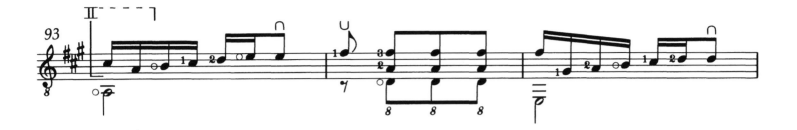

2. Fantasie

Original key: C Minor
⑥ to D

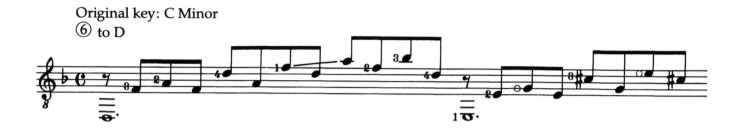

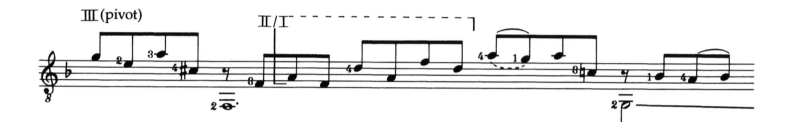

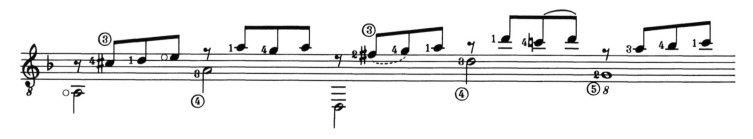

9

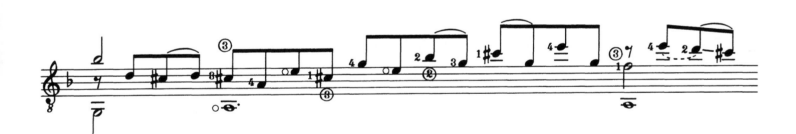

10

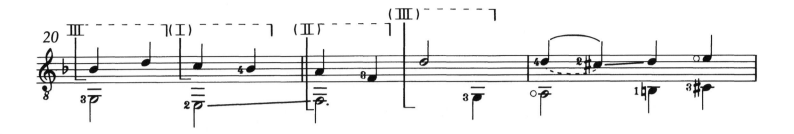

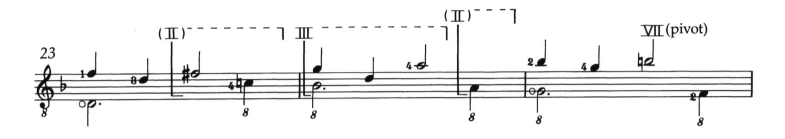

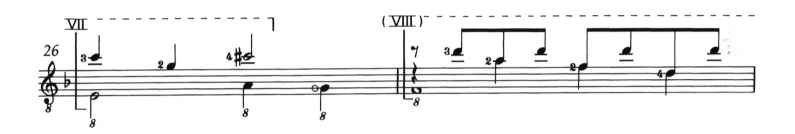

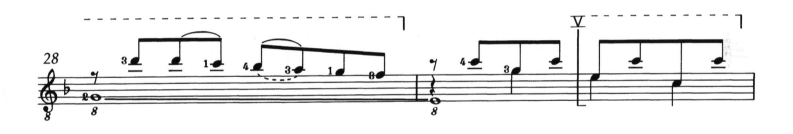

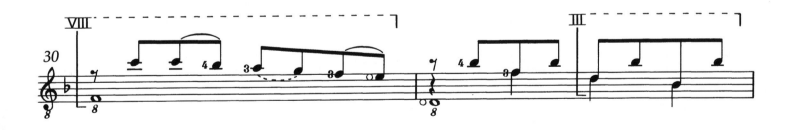

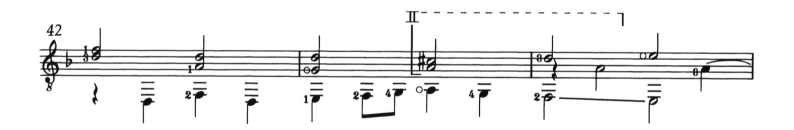

Weiss 1719 à Prague

3. Tombeau sur la Mort de Mur. Comte d'Logy

Arrivée 1721
Composée par Silvio Leopold Weiss

Original key: B flat Minor

Adagio

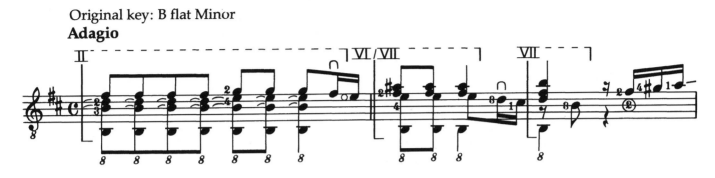

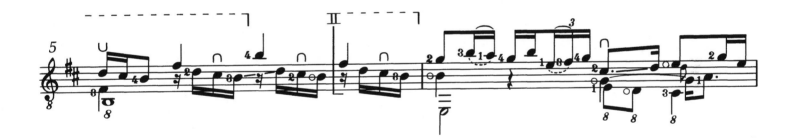

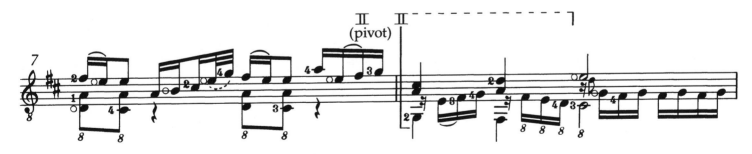

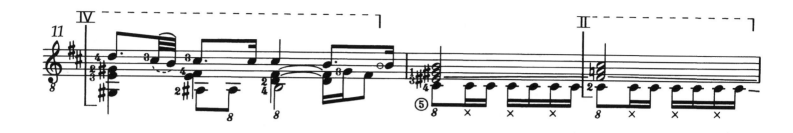

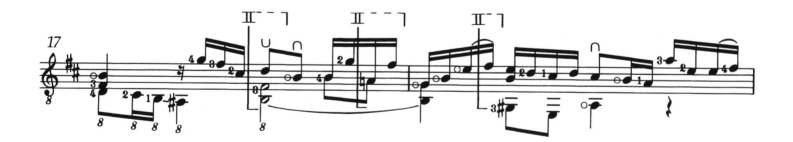

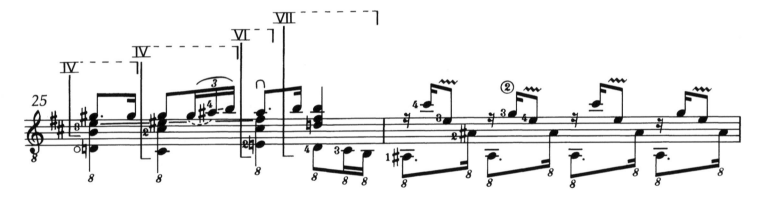

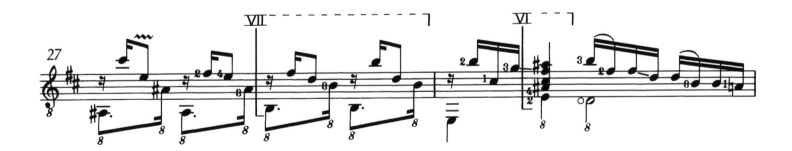

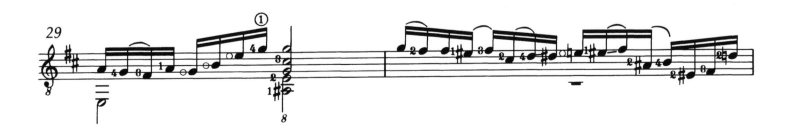

4. Capricio

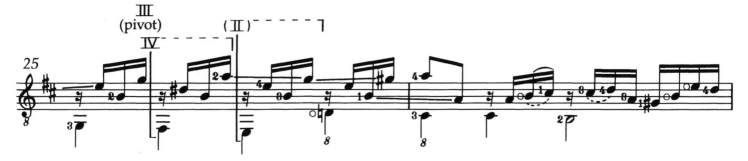

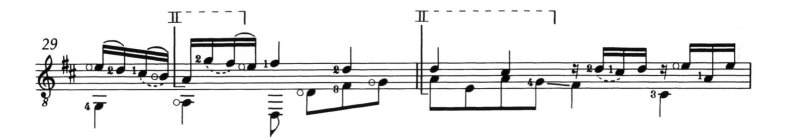

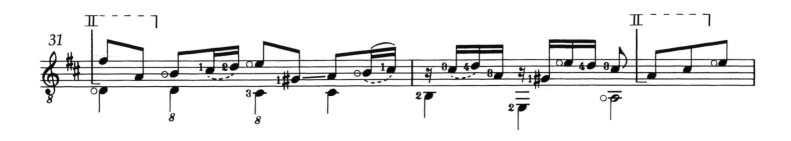

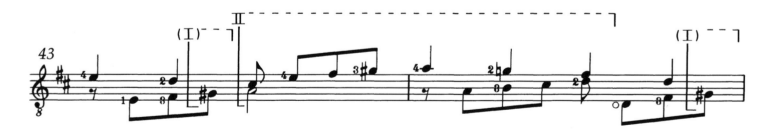

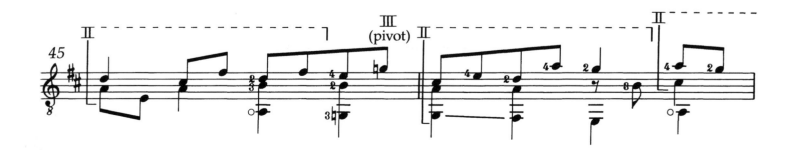

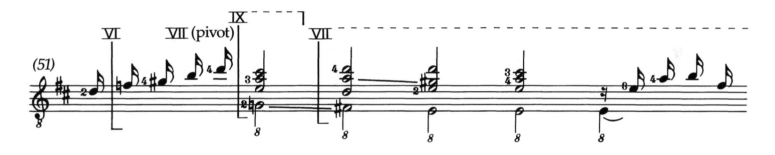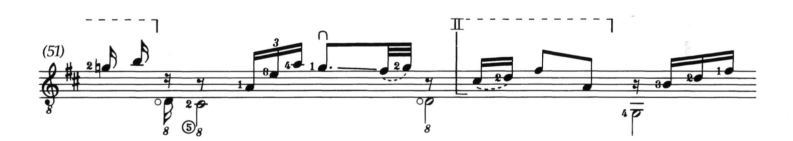

5. Ciacona

Original key: G Minor

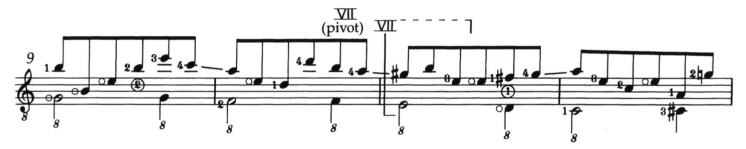

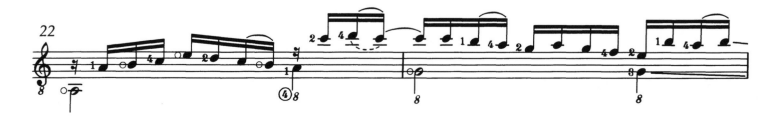

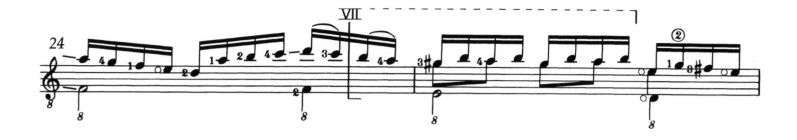

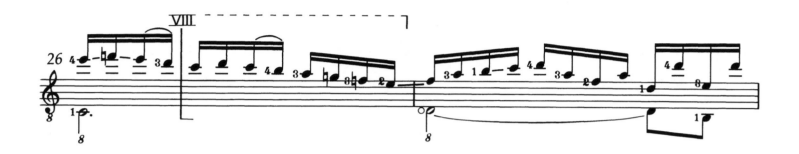

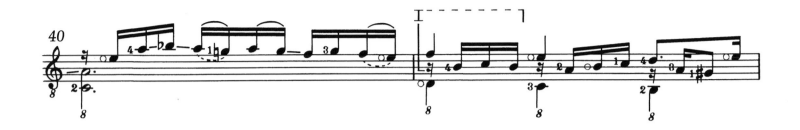

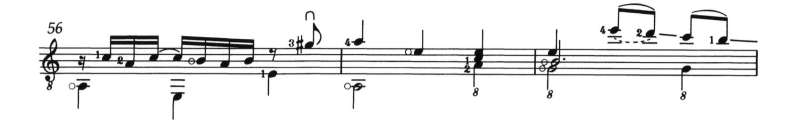

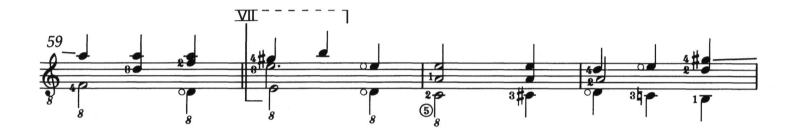

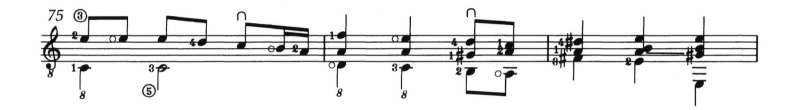

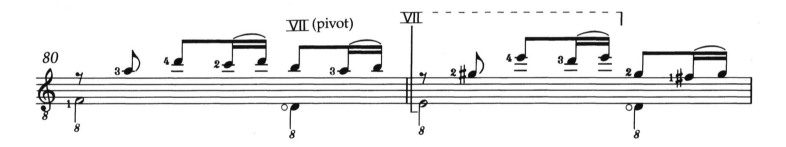

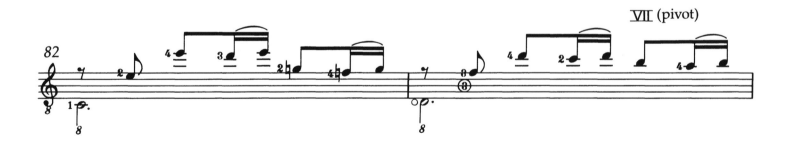

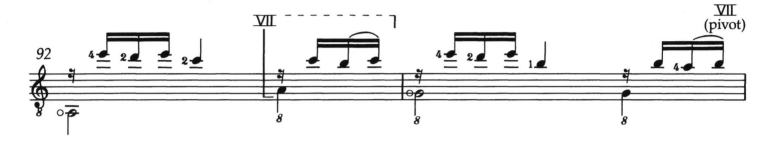

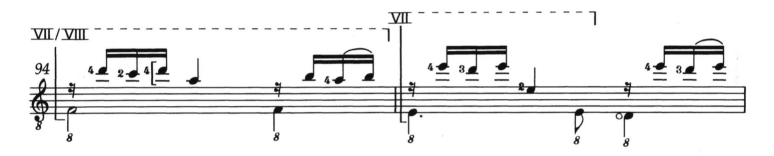

6. Fuga

Original key
⑥ to D

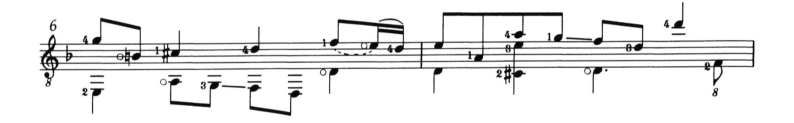

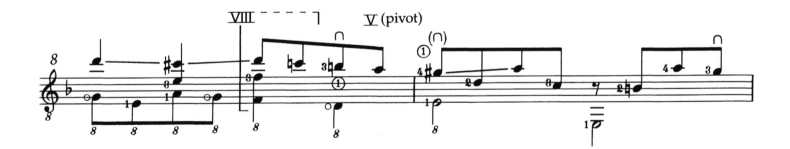

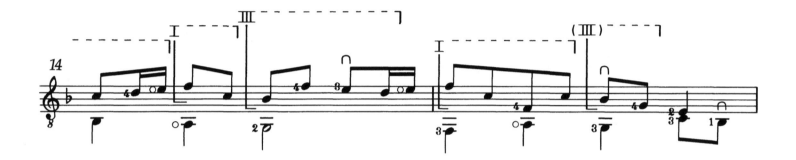

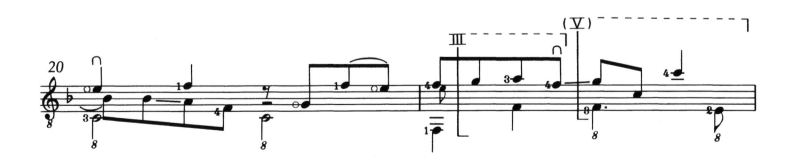

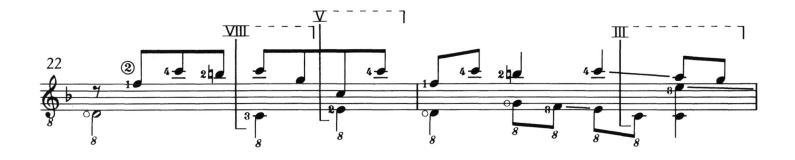

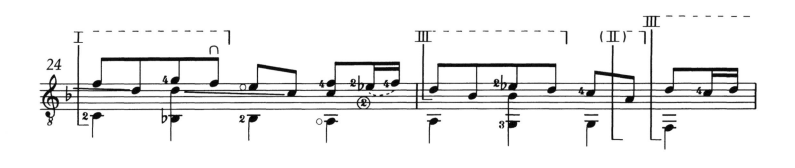

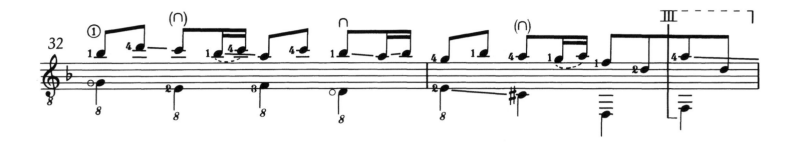

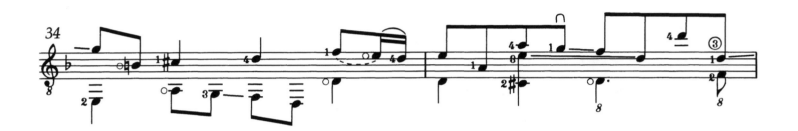

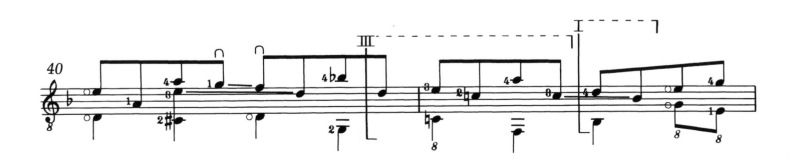

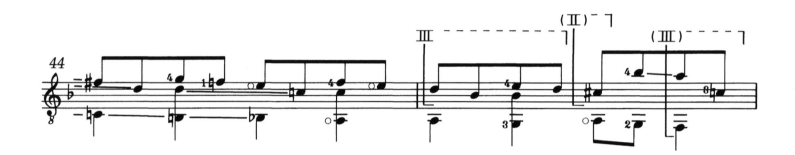

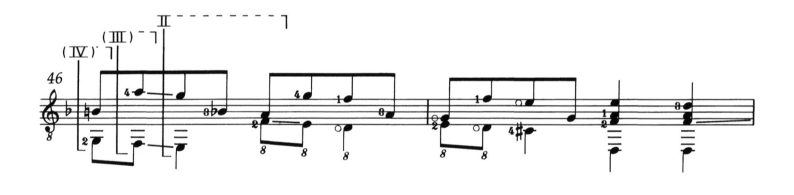

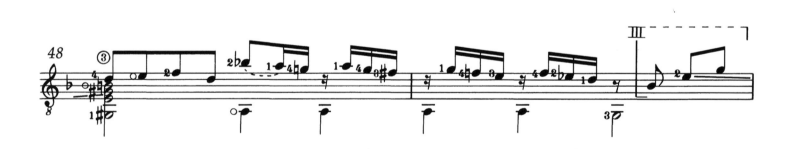

7. Tombeau sur la Mort de M: Cajetan Baron d'Hartig

Arrivée le 25 de mars 1719
Composée par Silvio Leopold Weiss à Dresden

Original key: E flat Minor
⑥ to D

Adagio assai

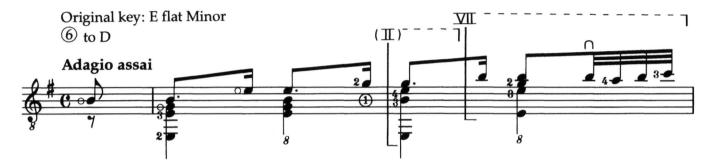

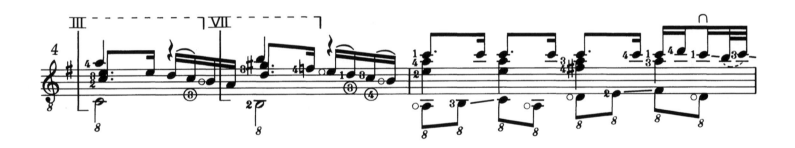

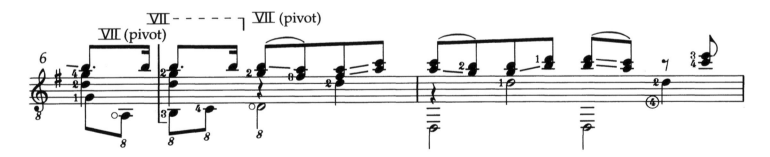

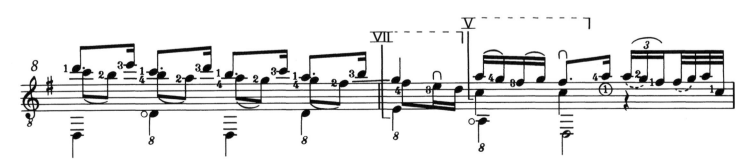

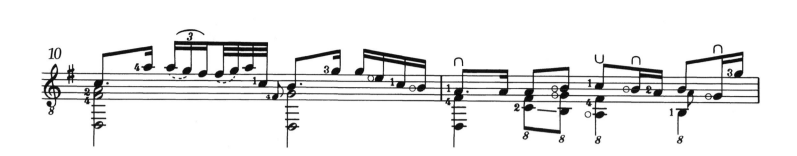

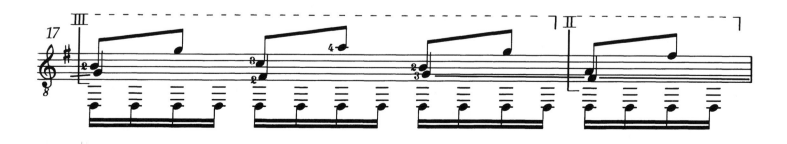

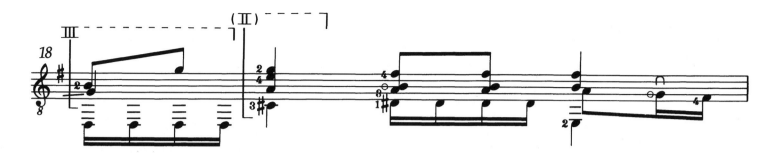

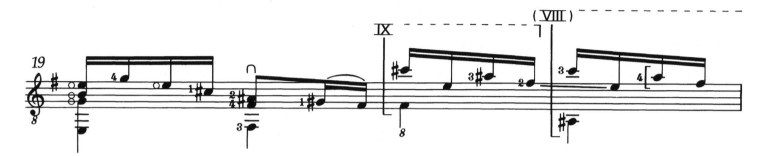

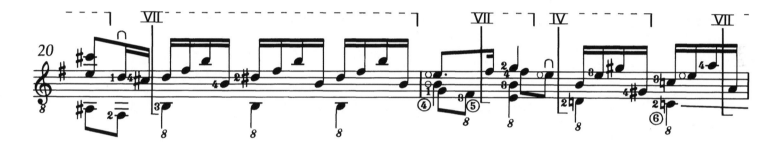

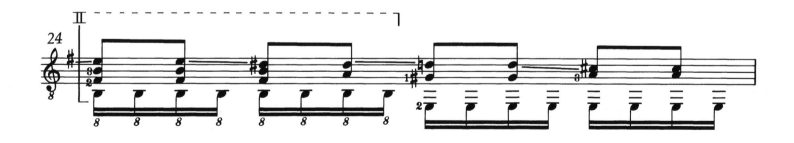

8. Passagaille

Original key
⑥ to D

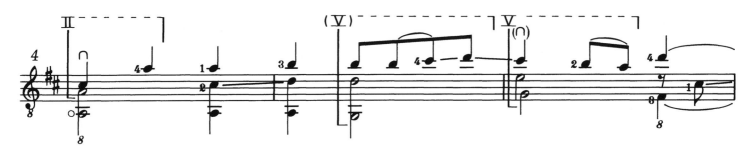

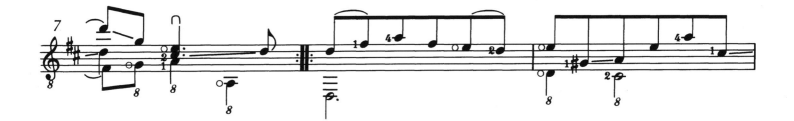

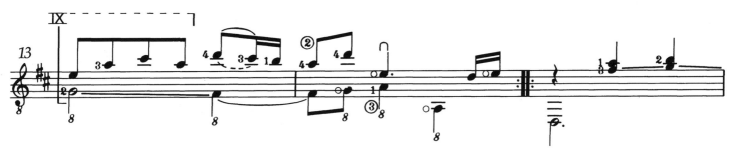

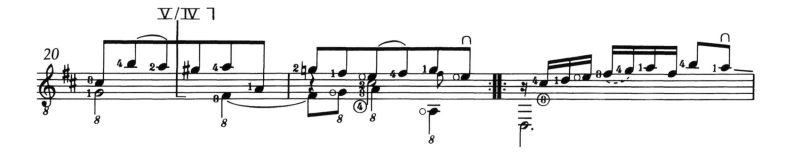

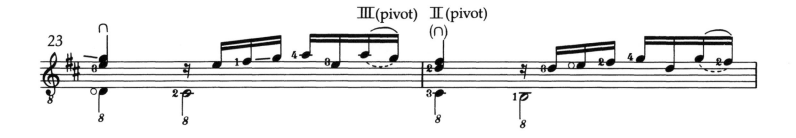

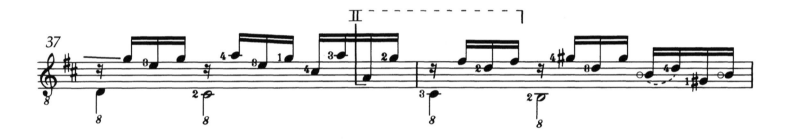

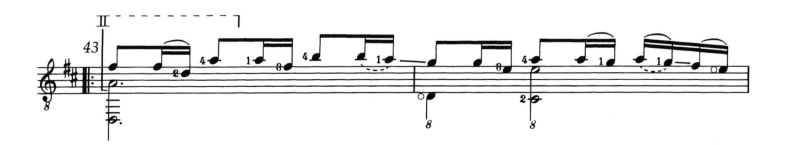

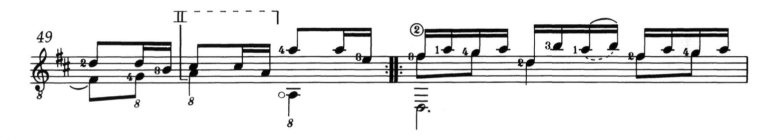

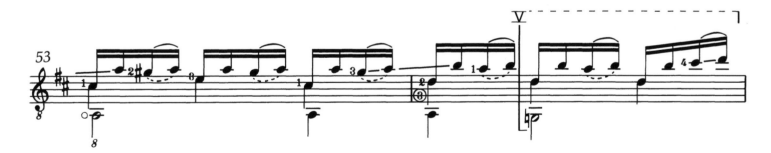

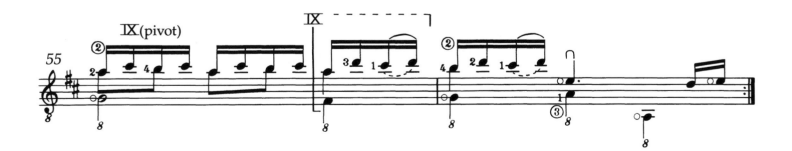

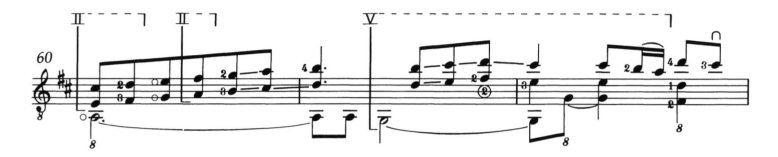

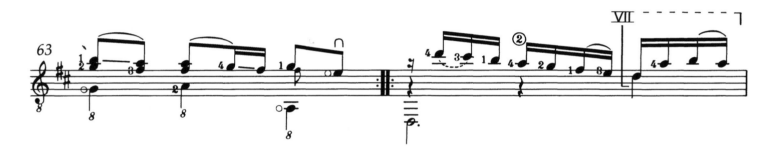

Schott Music Ltd., London S&Co.8169